CONTENTS

Mammals

Fish

Reptiles

Dinosaurs

Invertebrates

Amphibians

Birds

Marvellous Mammals

On the ground, in the air and underwater, mammals can be found everywhere. Read on to discover some fascinating facts about this varied class of animals.

What is a mammal?

Mammals are **warm-blooded**, have **fur** or **hair** and the females have glands that give **milk**. Elephants, dogs, bats, whales and **even humans** are all classed as mammals.

World's Fastest

The **cheetah** is the fastest animal over a short distance. It can reach a speedy **87 km/h** (54 mph) – that's almost as fast as a heavy goods vehicle driving along a motorway.

The **three-toed sloth** that can be found in tropical South America is probably the slowest mammal in the world. Its average ground speed is just **1.8-2.4m** (6-8ft) per minute.

Longest Living

After humans, the Asian elephant is the longest living land mammal. The oldest recorded is a male elephant called Lin Wang who lived to the grand old age of **86 years**.

Elephants can detect thunderstorms.

Looking Down

The tallest living animal is the **giraffe**. The average adult stands tall at **4.7- 5.3m** (15ft 5in – 17ft 5in).

A giraffe can lick its own eyes!

The **capybara**, found in northern South America, is the giant of the rodent world. It looks a bit like a huge guinea pig.

The **African bush elephant** is the largest living land animal. An average adult measures **3-3.7m** (9ft 10in-12ft) and weighs a hefty **4-7 tonnes**.

Food for Thought

The **giant panda** has to spend up to **15 hours a day** feeding in order to survive.

The smallest mammal in the world is the **Kitti's hog-nosed bat.**

The 'Most Fussy Eater' award goes to the **koala** of eastern Australia which eats only eucalyptus leaves.

Bottlenose dolphins can turn somersaults.

Wonderful Whales

Majestic whales are the giants of the ocean. Let's find out more about these enormous mammals.

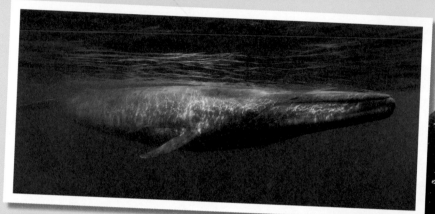

Record Breaker

The **blue whale** is the heaviest and largest animal on Earth. The average adult length is **25m** (80ft) for males and **26.2m** (86ft) for females, which is longer than two double decker buses! A blue whale's average weight is **90-120 tonnes**.

Southern right whales, **humpbacks** and **killer whales** are well known for their acrobatics. Humpbacks have been known to leap out of the water **70-80** times in a row.

Diving Deep

Cuvier's beaked whales are known as extreme divers. They often dive as deep as **2000m** (6560ft) and one has been recorded diving to a record depth of **2992m** (9816ft).

Big Babies

Blue whale babies grow 1000 times faster than human babies in the womb. Once born, blue whale calves drink **200 litres** (360 pints) of their mother's milk every day.

A blue whale's blow reaches a height of 15m (50ft).

Let's do Lunch

The hungry **blue whale** eats up to **5.5 tonnes** of food a day – that's the same weight as an African elephant.

Killer whale

Nice and Noisy

Blue whales can communicate with each other across enormous stretches of ocean by giving off low-frequency pulses. The sounds can be heard by other whales up to **3000km** (1850 miles) away.

The male **humpback whale** sings the longest and most complex songs in the animal kingdom. Each song lasts up to an hour and a half.

The sperm whale has the world's heaviest brain.

The average humpback whale weighs the same as 400 people.

Animal Hunt

Can you find the names of these animals hidden in the wordsearch below? Tick a box as you spot each one.

Names can go down, across, diagonally and backwards.

F	H	A	S	C	A	N	B	W	K
S	O	I	O	A	T	T	E	A	R
E	P	X	R	M	K	E	F	L	A
V	S	A	E	E	E	A	E	R	V
I	W	O	C	L	N	T	A	U	D
T	I	I	O	D	G	W	R	S	R
H	Y	E	N	A	A	N	I	B	A
G	C	E	I	T	R	R	G	H	A
E	H	I	H	M	O	L	E	O	H
N	T	S	R	W	O	R	E	E	D

Animals with hooves are called ungulates.

☐ Giraffe

☐ Hyena

☑ Deer

☑ Walrus

☐ Aardvark

☑ Fox

☐ Rhinoceros

☐ Camel

☑ Mole

☐ Kangaroo

Super Sequences

Look carefully at the sequences below.
Can you work out which animal completes each one?

1

2

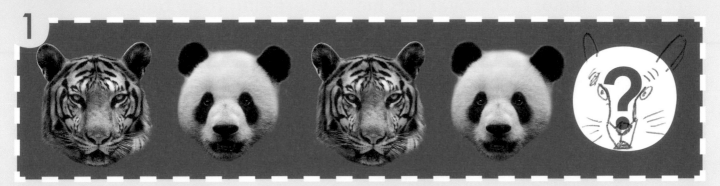

3

4

Answers on pages 76–77

Meet the Primates

There are around 400 species of primates including monkeys, apes and lemurs. Discover lots more interesting facts below.

Super Small

The world's smallest primate is the **pygmy mouse lemur**. This tiny creature isn't much bigger than an overweight mouse with a head/body length of **6.2cm** (2^7/$_{16}$ in) and a tail length of **13.6cm** (5^7/$_{16}$ in).

6.2 cm

Two species of **orangutan** are the largest tree-living mammals on Earth. Found on only two Indonesian islands, the females have an average height of **1.15m** (46in) while the males stand tall at **1.37m** (54in).

Apes can be trained to use simple sign language.

The **gorilla** is the largest of all primates. It can reach a standing height of up to **1.95m** (6ft 5in) and has an impressive chest measurement of as much as **1.98m** (78in).

All apes, except humans, have exceptionally long arms.

One of the Family

The closest relatives to humans are **chimpanzees** and **bonobos.** We have about **99%** of the same genes and share similar qualities such as empathy and being able to work in a team.

Primates learn behaviour by watching and copying one another.

Red vakari

Proboscis monkey

Make Some Noise

The howler money is one of the loudest mammals in the world. A male's cry can be heard at least **3km** (2 miles) away through the jungle and **5km** (3 miles) away across water.

Emperor tamarin

Brilliant Bats

Read on to find out more about these flying, night time creatures.

The oldest bat skeletons date from about 52 million years ago.

Big Bats

The biggest bats in the world are the **flying foxes**. Many species have a wing span of at least **1.7m** (5ft 7in).

The **Kitti's hog-nosed bat** is the smallest with a wingspan of **15-16cm** (6-6$\frac{1}{3}$ in). Its body is about the same size as a bumble bee.

Fruit bats live in colonies of up to 8 million.

Feeding Time

Vampire bats feed only on the blood of other animals. They feast at night when their victims are asleep and, because their bite is normally painless, the victims don't usually wake up. It takes about **20 minutes** for a vampire bat to drink the blood it needs.

Chilling Out

In the cold winter bats either migrate to warmer places or hibernate. Many hibernating bats allow their bodies to cool to almost freezing point. The North American **red bat**, which has the thickest fur of any bat, can withstand its body tissues actually freezing into ice.

All Aboard

The female **red bat** is the strongest flier. She can even carry two or three infants clinging to her fur.

Most bats give birth to only one young at a time.

Echo, Echo, Echo...

Clever bats use echolocation, the echoes of their calls and clicks, to detect objects in their path. From this they are able to tell distance, size and shape. Some species are able to detect objects as small as midges from at least **20m** (65 ft away).

Mammal Match

Only one of these giraffes matches the one in the leaf shape exactly. Can you work out which one it is?

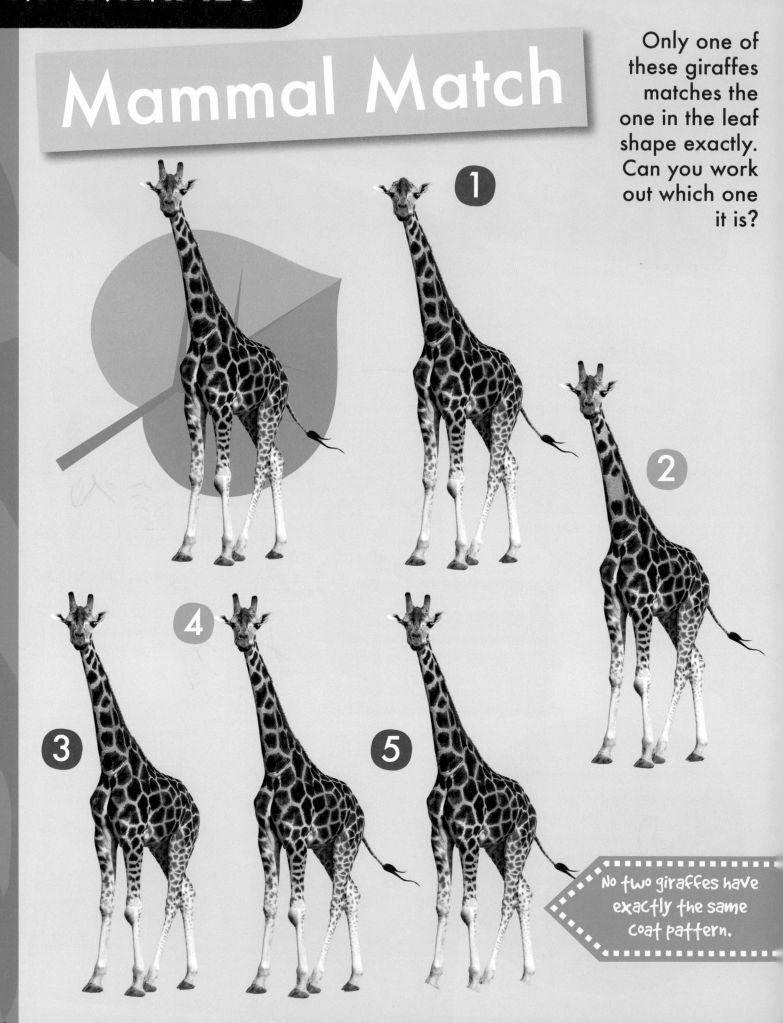

No two giraffes have exactly the same coat pattern.

The American antelope holds a land animal world record. Match the coloured letters to the boxes below to discover what it's for.

Colour Code

C N S E A O V
F R T L G D I

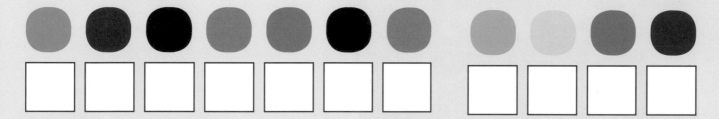

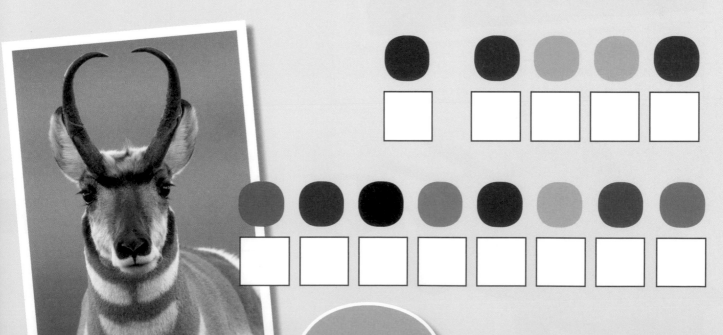

The American antelope sheds its horns every year.

Answers on pages 76–77

Mighty Dinosaurs

Dinosaurs ruled the Earth for over 160 million years. Find out more about these astonishing creatures below.

Long, Long Ago

Dinosaurs first appeared on Earth around **225 million years** ago in the Mesozoic Era. During the three time periods of this era (Triassic, Jurassic and Cretaceous) the land gradually split from one huge continent into smaller ones.

Feeling Hungry

Most dinosaurs were plant-eating herbivores but some of the more ferocious ones were meat-eating carnivores.

Extreme Lengths

One of the longest dinosaurs was the plant-eating **Diplodocus**. With its enormous neck and tail it measured about **26m** (85ft), the same as three buses. The longest meat-eater was the fearsome **Spinosaurus** which was up to **18m** (60ft), about the length of two buses.

Stegosaurus only had a tiny brain, about the size of a plum.

Tyrannosaurus could crunch through bone.

Standing Tall

One of the tallest dinosaurs was the **Brachiosaurus** which was a staggering **30m** (98ft 5in) high. It's likely that this giant ate leaves from tall tree-like plants.

Changing Times

Throughout their existence dinosaurs took on a huge variety of forms and evolved to adapt to changes in the environment. Species that failed to adapt to the new conditions became extinct.

Dinosaurs had straight legs, perpendicular to their bodies, which allowed them to move faster than other reptiles.

End of an Era

After dominating the land for over **160 million years**, dinosaurs became extinct **66 million years** ago. It is unknown exactly how this happened but, as it was over a relatively short period of time, it seems likely there was a catastrophic event, such as an asteroid impact or volcanic eruptions, that changed the environment more quickly than the dinosaurs could adapt.

DINOSAURS

Dino Fact Files

Read on to discover more about some of the most well-known dinosaurs.

Name: Tyrannosaurus
(*tie-RAN-oh-sore-us*)

Meaning of name: Tyrant lizard

Length: 12m (39ft 4in)

Weight: 7 tonnes

Diet: Carnivore

Time period: Late Cretaceous (67-66 million years ago)

Found in: Canada, USA

Description: A fearsome animal with a powerful jaw. It had 60 teeth, each one up to 20cm (8in) long and its bite was around three times as powerful as a lion's. It used its sharp sense of smell to hunt live prey and locate carcasses to scavenge. It walked on two legs and had an enormous skull over 1.5m (5ft) long.

Name: Stegosaurus (*STEG-oh-SORE-us*)

Meaning of name: Roof lizard

Length: 9m (29½ ft)

Diet: Herbivore

Time period: Late Jurassic (156-145 million years ago)

Found in: USA

Description: A slow-moving plant eater which would have used its powerful spiked tail to defend itself from predators. It had bony plates along its back which may have warned off attackers or been used to regulate body temperature.

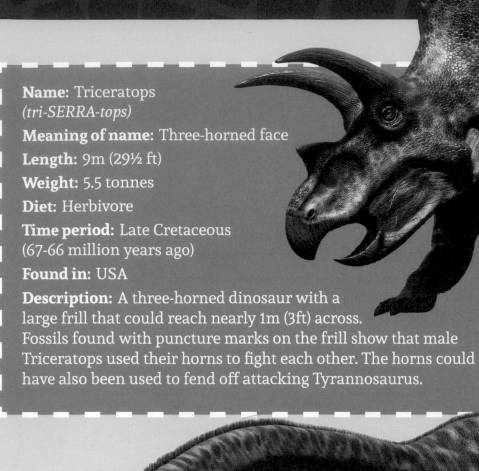

Name: Triceratops
(tri-SERRA-tops)

Meaning of name: Three-horned face

Length: 9m (29½ ft)

Weight: 5.5 tonnes

Diet: Herbivore

Time period: Late Cretaceous
(67-66 million years ago)

Found in: USA

Description: A three-horned dinosaur with a large frill that could reach nearly 1m (3ft) across. Fossils found with puncture marks on the frill show that male Triceratops used their horns to fight each other. The horns could have also been used to fend off attacking Tyrannosaurus.

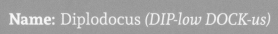

Name: Diplodocus *(DIP-low DOCK-us)*

Meaning of name: Double beam

Length: 26m (85ft 4in)

Diet: Herbivore

Time period: Late Jurassic
(156-145 million years ago)

Found in: USA

Description: A long-tailed dinosaur with a long neck which would have been used to reach high and low vegetation and drink water. Its tail would have been held high to balance the neck.

DINOSAURS

Picture Puzzle

Use the dinosaur key to follow the correct path through the maze from start to finish.

RIGHT

LEFT

DOWN

START

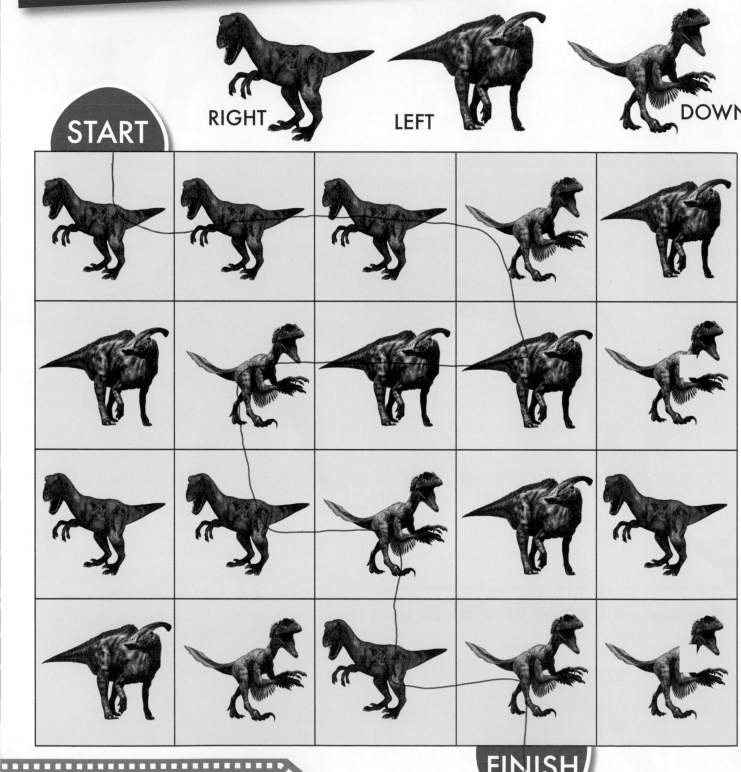

FINISH

Around 25 different species of dinosaur lived in the UK.

How many words can you make from the letters in DINOSAUR? Write your answers below.

Dinosaur Words

DINOSAUR

1 NO

2 DINO

3 SO

4 ON

5 IN

6 our

7

8

9

10

How did you do?
0-2 words: Not bad!
3-5 words: Great job!
More than 5 words: Awesome!

The smallest dinosaurs were only about the size of a turkey.

Answers on pages 76-77

Fascinating Fish

There are thousands of species of fish living in the world's oceans and rivers. Read on for lots of interesting fish facts.

World's Biggest

The largest fish in the world is the **whale shark** which lives in the tropical and warm waters of the Atlantic, Pacific and Indian Oceans. Experts believe they can measure up to **12m** (40ft).

The shortest and lightest recorded species of fish in the world is the *Paedocypris progenetica* from Southeast Asia. Females grow to just **7.9mm** ($^5/_{16}$ in).

A Quick Snack

The award for fastest eating fish goes to the **frogfish**, which can be found in tropical and sub-tropical waters around the world. Frogfish use their mouths like a vacuum cleaner to suck their prey inside. The whole thing is over in just under **six milliseconds**.

Sea horses are the slowest-moving marine fish.

Out of the Water

Not all fish live only in the water. **Mudskippers** spend most of their time in tropical mudflats and mango swamps, where they scurry about in the mud. They return to the water every few minutes to wet their skin and take in a mouthful of water.

Ready to Bite

Piranhas are said to be the most ferocious freshwater fish in the world. With their razor sharp teeth and powerful jaws, they will attack any creature, regardless of size.

The Indian Stonefish has spines sharp enough to pierce the sole of a beach shoe.

Archer fish can shoot insects down from leaves and branches by spitting a jet of water at them.

Electric Fish

More than **250** species of fish can generate electric pulses. These are used for a number of reasons, including communication and to stun or kill predators or prey. The most powerful electric fish is the **electric eel** which can emit enough electricity to stun a horse.

Underwater Observation

These two pictures may look the same but there are 10 differences between them. Can you spot them all?

About 100 new species of fish are discovered every year.

Tick a box as you find each difference.

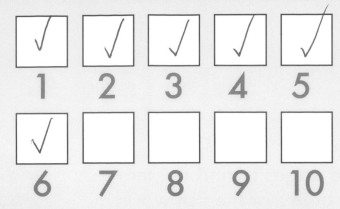

1 2 3 4 5
6 7 8 9 10

Answers on pages 76-77

Super Sharks

Read these pages to find out more about the giants of the fish world.

There are more than 500 species of sharks.

Shark Survival
Sharks can survive for long periods of time without eating. Even the most active species can fast for six weeks or more.

Huge Appetite
The **tiger shark** has been nicknamed 'garbage-can shark' because it will eat anything it comes across in the water, including a wide variety of fish, seabirds and domestic animals that happen to fall in. Unusual items found in the stomachs of tiger sharks include car tyres, wristwatches and paint cans!

Caribbean reef shark

Despite their bad image, most sharks are harmless to people.

Fastest Swimmer

Most sharks are slow swimmers, only speeding up for short bursts when chasing prey. The fastest shark is believed to be the **shortfin mako** which may be able to swim as fast as **88 km/h** (55 mph).

Sense of Smell

Sharks have a much better sense of smell than any other fish. They can detect blood from great distances, sniffing out the equivalent of a few drops of blood in an Olympic-sized swimming pool. It is said sharks can even smell other fish's fear!

Big Bite

The **great white shark** has the strongest bite of any living species. It is thought to exert a force of more than **1.8 tonnes.**

Thresher sharks have tail fins as long as their bodies.

Make a Match

Draw lines to match these fish into pairs. Which one doesn't have a match?

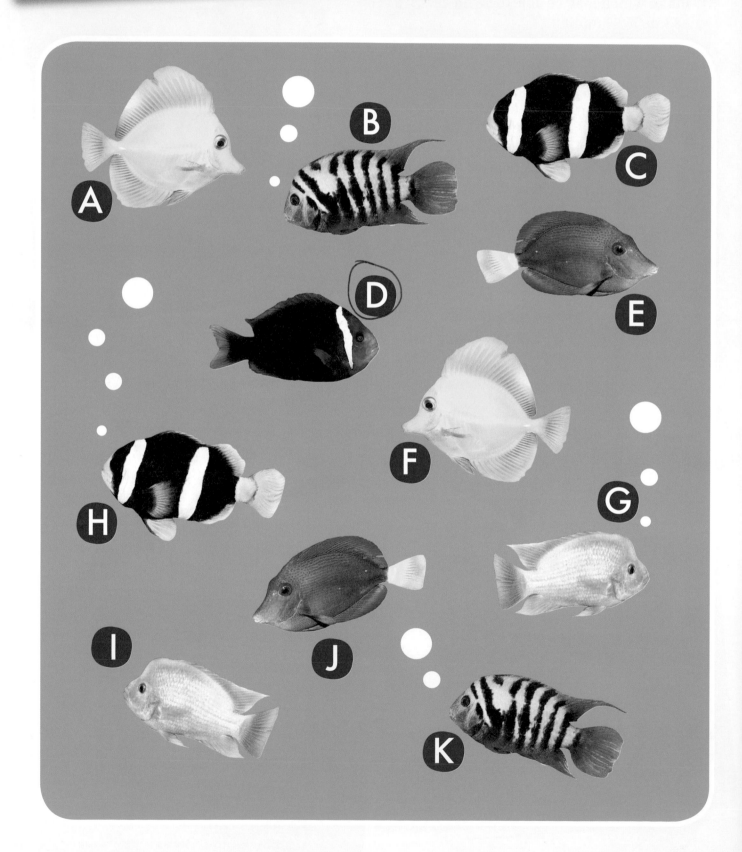

A B C D E F G H I J K

Underwater Words

Something fishy has happened to the underwater words below and they've been scrambled up! Can you work out what each one is supposed to say?

Write your answers in the boxes. Some of the letters have been added to help you.

1

F	S	I	H

F	i	S	H

2

C	R	A	O	L

C	O	R	A	L

3

A	S	E

S	E	A

4

A	W	E	T	R

W	A	T	E	R

The oldest fish fossils discovered are 420 million years old.

5

S	W	E	A	E	E	D

S	E	A	W	E	E	D

6

O	C	K	R

R	O	C	K

7

R	F	E	E

R	E	E	F

8

A	N	D	S

S	A	N	D

Answers on pages 76–77

Meet the Reptiles

Slithering snakes, ginormous crocodiles and long-tongued lizards are all part of the reptile kingdom. Read on for some amazing reptile facts.

What is a reptile?

Reptiles have **dry, scaly skin** and lay eggs on land. Snakes, crocodiles, turtles and lizards are all classed as **reptiles**.

The first crocodiles appeared 240 million years ago.

Lengthy Reptile

The largest living reptile in the world is the **saltwater crocodile**. Males are mature when they reach a length of about **3.2m** (10ft 6in) and females when they reach about **2.2m** (7ft 3in) and they continue to grow for many years afterwards. It's thought possible for saltwater crocs to reach extreme lengths of **9-10m** (29½-33ft) which is about the same as two family cars.

The smallest reptile is the **dwarf gecko**. It measures just **1.6cm** (⅝in) from snout to vent with a tail of about the same length and is tiny enough to sit on a fingertip.

Actual size!

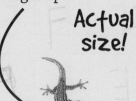

World Record

The greatest age that any land animal has lived to is **175 years** for a **Galapagos giant turtle** called Harriet. DNA testing suggests she hatched in 1830.

Dealing with Danger

Three species of **horned lizard** can change colour to match the desert sand and inflate themselves to look more intimidating when feeling threatened.

A number of snakes, including the **European grass snake**, pretend to be dead when danger strikes.

Phrynosoma solare lizard

The plumed basilisk lizard can run across water without sinking.

Lizard Tails

The longest lizard in the world is the **Salvadori** or **Papupan monitor** which has been measured in lengths up to **4.75m** (15ft 7in). Nearly 70% of its length is taken up by its long tail.

Tortoises and turtles don't have any teeth.

Most lizard species are able to shed their tails when faced with danger, such as their tail being grasped by a predator. Eventually the lost tail will regrow. There's no limit to the number of times a lizard can regrow its tail.

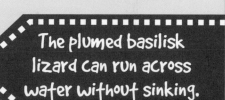

S-s-s-nakes!

Hissing snakes can be found around the world. Discover more facts about these wriggling reptiles below.

Most snakes only feed once a week.

Looking Long

The longest snake is the **reticulated python** which regularly exceeds lengths of **6.25m** (20 ½ft). The longest venomous snake is the **king cobra** which averages **3.7-4.6m** (12-15ft).

The world's shortest snakes are the **thread snakes**. There are about 100 species and they're all shorter than **40cm** (16in). The tiniest of all is the rare *Leptotyphlops carlae* which is about **10cm** (4in) long and as thin as a strand of spaghetti.

Where in the World?

Australia has more venomous snakes than any other country in the world. Out of the 187 species found there, around 120 species are venomous. Several countries and islands, including Iceland, New Zealand and Ireland, don't have any snakes at all.

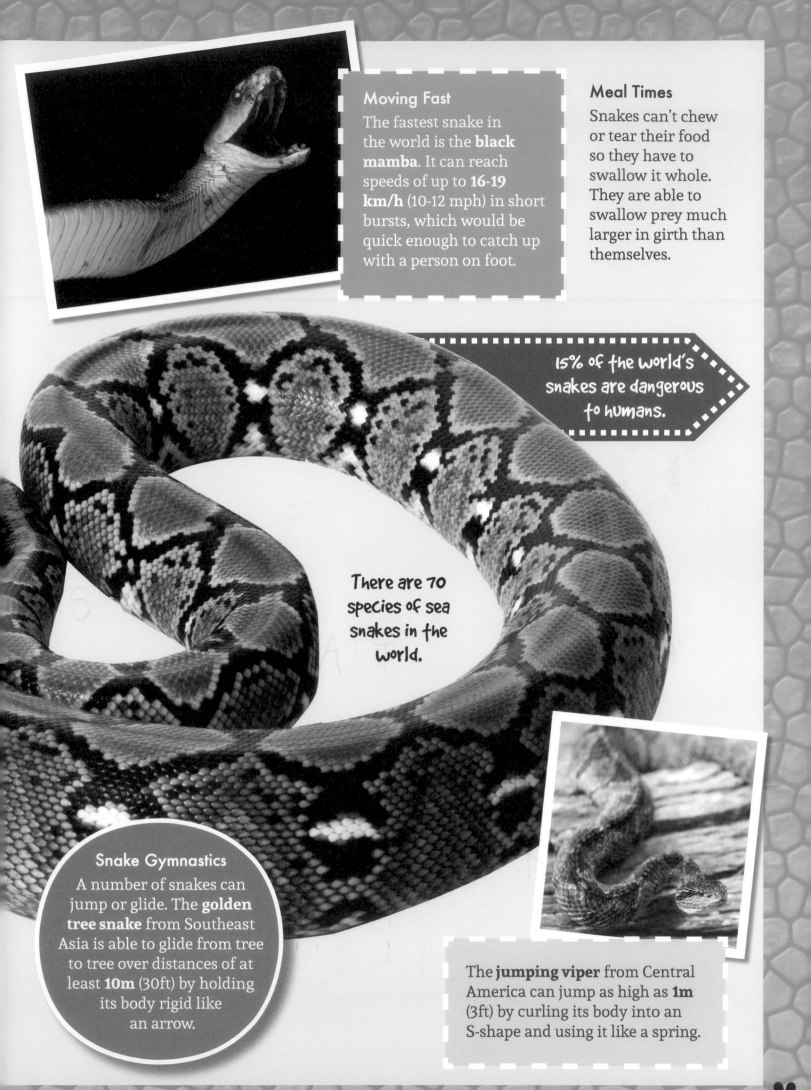

Moving Fast
The fastest snake in the world is the **black mamba**. It can reach speeds of up to **16-19 km/h** (10-12 mph) in short bursts, which would be quick enough to catch up with a person on foot.

Meal Times
Snakes can't chew or tear their food so they have to swallow it whole. They are able to swallow prey much larger in girth than themselves.

15% of the world's snakes are dangerous to humans.

There are 70 species of sea snakes in the world.

Snake Gymnastics
A number of snakes can jump or glide. The **golden tree snake** from Southeast Asia is able to glide from tree to tree over distances of at least **10m** (30ft) by holding its body rigid like an arrow.

The **jumping viper** from Central America can jump as high as **1m** (3ft) by curling its body into an S-shape and using it like a spring.

Tortoise Time

Starting with the smallest, can you put these tortoises into order of size? Write your answers in the boxes.

A

B

C

D

E

F

The oldest recorded land animal was a giant tortoise that lived to 175 years old.

SMALLEST | | | | | BIGGEST

| B | F | A | E | C | D |

Can you piece the broken parts of this image back together to work out which animal is in the picture?

Bits and Pieces

Warning! Two of the pieces don't fit in the image.

Answers on pages 76–77

Crocodiles and Alligators

These pages are packed with fascinating facts about these powerful predators.

Reptile Family
Crocodiles and **alligators** belong to the crocodilia order of reptiles. Crocodilians are distinguished by their **long jaws, short legs** and **powerful tail**.

A crocodilians jaw can be kept closed with a rubber band.

On the Go
A few species of crocodilians are able to gallop on land. The fastest ever recorded is the **freshwater crocodile** which can reach running speeds of up to **17 km/h** (10½ mph).

Heading Home
Clever crocodiles are able to find their way back home over long distances and through unknown terrain. In a study, three wild crocodiles were taken hundreds of kilometres from their homes in northern Queensland, Australia, before being released. They each made it back to their home rivers.

Reptile Roars

Crocodilians are the noisiest of all reptiles. They can make a wide range of coughs, hisses, roars and bellows. The loudest of all is the **American alligator** whose bellow can be easily heard from a distance of **150m** (500ft).

crocodilians can tackle prey bigger than themselves.

Chilly Waters

The **Chinese alligator** and the **American alligator** live in areas where the temperature can fall below freezing during the winter. If they stay in the water, they keep the tip of their snout exposed and allow the rest of their head and upper body to be frozen into the ice. They can survive like this until the ice melts.

Most crocodilians only stay underwater for a few minutes at a time.

Turtles and Tortoises

With their long necks and large shells, turtles and tortoises are fascinating to look at. Let's find out some facts about these interesting creatures.

Reptile Family

Along with **terrapins**, **turtles** and **tortoises** belong to the testudines or chelonia order of reptiles. **Chelonians** are distinguished by their shell of bony plates.

Many giant tortoises are thought to live to more than 100 years of age.

Aldabra giant tortoise

Slow Going

Tortoises are well-known for being extremely slow moving. Their large shells make it impossible to get anywhere in a hurry. Tests carried out on the **Californian giant tortoise** revealed a walking speed of **3-8m** (10-26ft) a minute and similar tests on an **Aldabra giant tortoise** showed it couldn't move quicker than **4.5m** (15ft) a minute.

The fastest chelonians are the **sea turtles**. The highest speed claimed is **35 km/h** (22 mph) by a **Pacific leatherback turtle**.

The first chelonians appeared on Earth at least 200 million years ago.

Diving Record

The deepest turtle dive recorded was made by a **leatherback turtle** off the coast of County Kerry, Ireland in 2006. It reached a depth of **1250m** (4100ft).

The longest recorded turtle dive of **10 hours and 14 minutes** was made by a **loggerhead turtle** in 2007.

Loggerhead turtles make long migrations of up to two years.

Freezing Cold

After hatching in late summer, **painted turtles** hide from predators and hibernate. Whenever the temperature falls below **-3 °C** (26.5 °F) the turtles freeze. During the changing winter temperatures, they freeze and thaw over and over again before coming out of hibernation in the spring. When frozen they show no movement, respiration, heart beat or blood circulation.

Super Strong

The well named **alligator snapping turtle** has amazingly powerful jaws. It would be able to remove a human finger or toe if given the opportunity!

REPTILES

Who is it?

Match the close-ups to the animals by writing the correct letter under each close-up.

A
Western green lizard

B
Chameleon

C
Snake

Red eared turtle
D

Crocodile
E

A chameleon's tongue can extend to more than its body length.

1 = _D_   2 = _E_   3 = _A_   4 = _B_   5 = _C_

Cross out the following from the grid below to reveal a fact about the Komodo dragon.

Hidden Fact

COUNTRIES   COLOURS

SHAPES   FOOD

~~FRANCE~~	IT	~~RED~~	~~CHEESE~~	~~IS~~
~~RECTANGLE~~	~~THE~~	~~JAPAN~~	~~BREAD~~	LARGEST
~~GREEN~~	~~PENTAGON~~	LIZARD	~~PIZZA~~	IN
~~YELLOW~~	THE	~~MEXICO~~	~~PURPLE~~	WORLD

The Komodo dragon fact is:

It is the Largest lizard in the world.

Answers on pages 76–77

The Invertebrates

From buzzing insects to swarming jellyfish, invertebrates can be found in all sorts of habitats. These pages reveal some amazing invertebrate facts.

What is an invertebrate?

An **invertebrate** is an animal that doesn't have a backbone. **Spiders, bees, butterflies** and **crabs** are among those classed as invertebrates.

Record Length

The longest known invertebrate, and indeed the longest known animal, in the world is the **boot-lace worm**. Found in the shallow waters of the North Sea, this super long worm has been measured at more than **55m** (180ft).

Look Closely

Squids are known for having large eyes. The biggest to date belonged to a colossal squid and measured **30-40cm** (11 ¾-15 ¾ in) in diameter.

Lots of Legs

Despite their names, **centipedes** don't have 100 legs and **millipedes** don't have a 1000. They do, however, have a lot of legs! The records are **375 pairs** (750 legs) for a millipede found in California, USA and **191 pairs** (382 legs) for a species of centipede from the Fiji Islands.

Most spiders only live for around a year.

Millipede

Super Sense

The **male emperor moth** is a world record holder for the best sense of smell. It can sniff out a female moth at a staggering range of **11km** (6¾ miles).

Octopuses are able to open screw top jars.

There are an estimated 5-10 million new species of insects yet to be found.

Jellyfish

Crab

Spider Facts

Long-legged spiders are often feared by humans, although few will actually cause any harm. Read on to discover some fascinating spider facts.

Most spiders live alone.

Long Legs

Many people think the **tarantula** is the world's largest spider but the biggest is in fact a species of **huntsman spider** found in Laos. The males have an enormous leg span of **30cm** (12in).

Australian Giant Huntsman

Midget spiders are the smallest known spiders. The tiniest is the male *Patu digua* which measures just **0.37mm** (¹⁄₆₄ in) long, excluding its mouthparts.

Jumping spiders have eight eyes.

Spiders can only run for a few seconds at a time.

The biggest webs are made by **golden orb-web** spiders. The largest which has been properly measured was **1.5m** (5ft) in circumference.

Wonderful Webs

It may look delicate but spider silk is the strongest of all natural and human-made fibres. It's so strong that catching a fly with a web is the equivalent of stopping a jet aircraft with a net just a few centimetres (an inch) thick.

The largest communal webs are built by *Ixeuticus socialis* spiders in Australia. These huge structures can measure up to **3.7m** (12ft 2in) in length and **1.2m** (3ft 11in) in width.

Pale Spitting spider

Jumping spider

Spitting Spiders

There are over 100 species of spitting spiders which produce a quick-setting glue to catch prey. A small amount of the glue is fired in streams from the spider's fangs, leaving prey stuck to the spot. It happens so quickly that it's impossible to see with the human eye.

Spider Sight

Most spiders have poor eyesight and aren't able to see much more than the difference between day and night. Instead they use touch and vibrations to work out what's happening in the world around them.

Tarantula

INVERTEBRATES

Which Way?

This spider wants to get back to its eggs. Can you guide it through the maze from start to finish?

START

FINISH

The silk of a garden spider is stronger than steel.

This army of ants is heading home. The quickest way is to follow the path where the numbers add up to the largest amount. Which path should they take?

On the Move

Ant columns can be up to 100m (110yd) long.

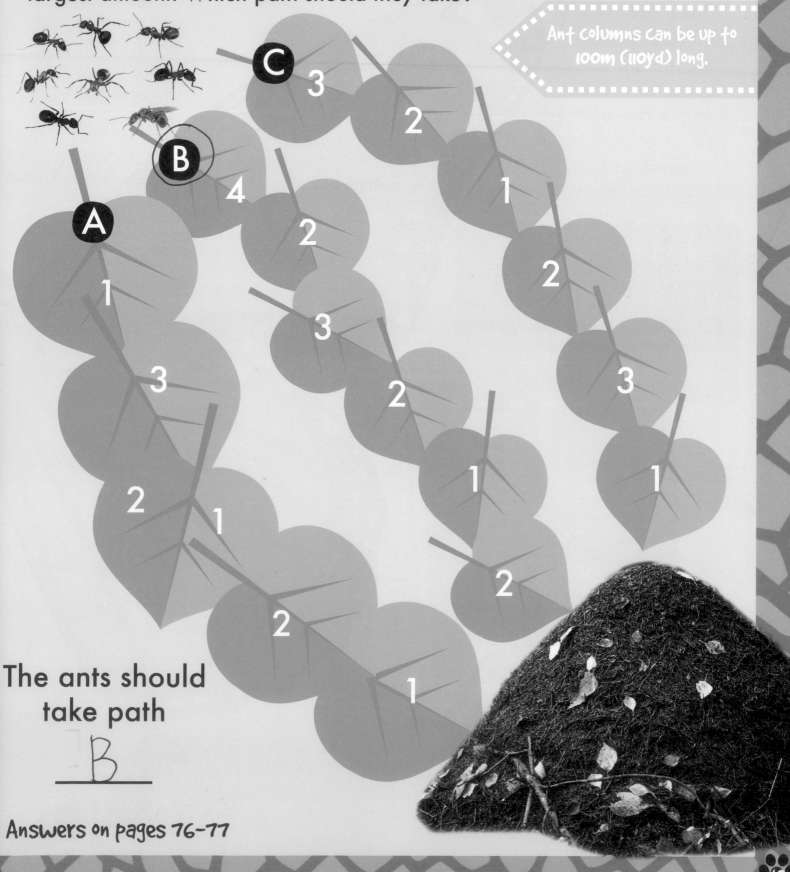

The ants should take path

B

Answers on pages 76–77

49

Beautiful Butterflies

There are over 20,000 known species of butterflies. These pages are packed full of other fascinating facts.

The monarch butterfly uses the sun as a compass when migrating.

Wide Wings

The biggest butterfly is the rare **Queen Alexandra's birdwing** from Papua New Guinea. The females are bigger than the males and can have a front wingspan of more than **28cm** (11in).

Most adult butterflies only live for two to three weeks.

The woolly bear caterpillar of the high Arctic spends up to 10 months a year frozen.

Meeting Up

Every November millions of **monarch butterflies** gather in forests along the coasts of California, USA and Mexico. The Californian colonies average more than 1000 butterflies per site and the Mexican colonies are much larger with millions of butterflies. Crowded together, they often cover every available space on the tree trunks and branches.

Peacock butterfly

Where in the World?

The rainforests of South America are home to the greatest diversity of butterflies in the world. Scientists recorded 1209 species in a **55km** (21¼ mile) area in Peru. Meanwhile, in the whole of Europe, there are less than 400 species.

Life Cycle

The life cycle of a butterfly (from egg to caterpillar and chrysalis to adult) can last for several years but the lifespan of the adult is much shorter than the other stages. Adult butterflies usually only live for a few weeks although some species can survive for up to nine months.

Quiet Creatures

Most butterflies are quiet creatures but the male butterflies in the *Hamadryas* genus make a loud clickety-clack sound that can be heard up to **30m** (100ft) away. The noise is produced when the butterflies' forewings collide during flight.

INVERTEBRATES

Who's Hiding?

Can you work out which creatures are hiding behind these leaves?

A Wasp

B Butterfly

C Beetle

D Spider

The bombardier beetle can let out an explosive puff of irritating gas from its bottom!

Spot the Sequence

The sequence highlighted below appears three more times in the grid. Can you spot where?

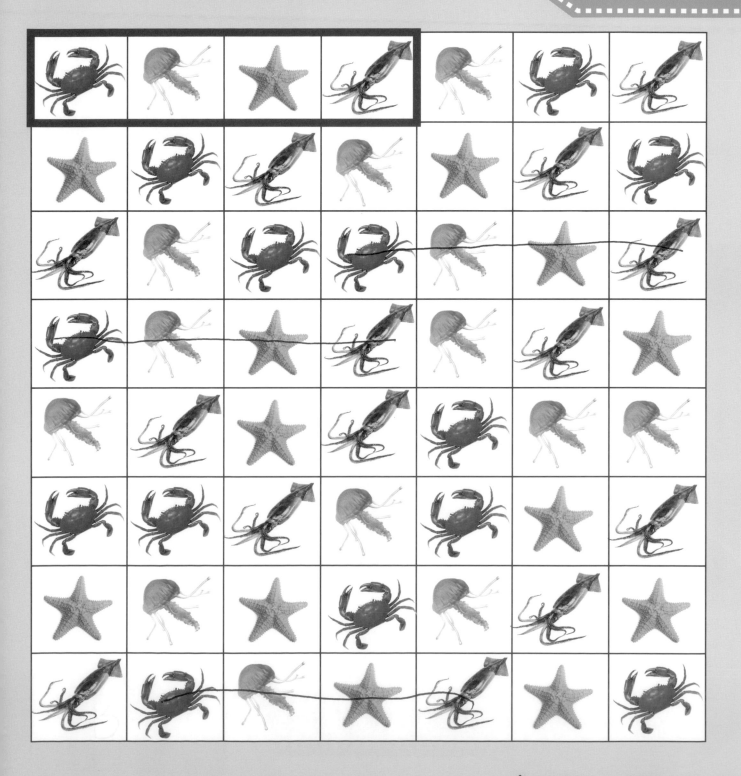

Answers on pages 76–77

Beautiful Birds

Birds of all shapes and sizes fill the sky with colour. Let's find out more about these featured creatures.

What is a bird?

A **bird** is a **warm-blooded animal** that can lay eggs. They have feathers, wings and a beak and most are able to fly. **Owls, flamingos, penguins** and **peacocks** are among those creatures classed as birds.

Bird Numbers

It is estimated that **150,000** bird species have lived on Earth since birds first evolved but nearly **94%** of them have become extinct. There are around **10,426** recognised species of bird alive today.

Big and Tall

The ostrich is the largest living bird in the world. The tallest is the **North African ostrich** which can measure up to **2.75m** (9ft).

A 9ft ostrich compared to a 6ft man

The smallest bird is widely claimed to be the **bee hummingbird** which has a body length of just **57mm** (2¼ in). However, some experts consider the little **woodstar** of southwest Columbia, Ecuador and northern Peru to be slightly smaller.

Making Nests

The smallest nests are built by tiny hummingbirds. The nest of the **bee hummingbird** is no bigger than a thimble.

The **sword-billed hummingbird** from South America has a bill that is longer than its body. Measuring **9-11cm** (3½-4½ in), its length enables the bird to collect nectar from plants with very deep trumpet-shaped flowers.

The emperor penguin lays the smallest egg in relation to the mother's size.

Big Bills
The impressive bill of the **Australian pelican** is the longest of any bird at **34-47cm** (13-18½ in).

13% of today's bird species are in danger of becoming extinct.

flamingo

Barn owl

Eagles make the biggest nests. One **golden eagle** nest, which was measured in Scotland in 1954, was **4.5m** (15ft) deep.

Flying High

From the fastest flier to the quickest wings, these pages will uncover lots of interesting facts about birds in flight.

Greatest Distance

The longest recorded non-stop flight was made by a **bar-tailed godwit** in 2007. It flew **11,680km** (7257 miles) in just over eight days – the equivalent of flying from the UK to Hawaii.

Fast Fliers

The fastest flying bird, and also the fastest animal of any kind, is the **peregrine falcon**. When diving from great heights it's able to reach a speed of at least **200 km/h** (124 mph) – that's as fast as a high speed train.

Bee hummingbird

Quickest Beat

Hummingbirds have the fastest wingbeats in the bird world. They move so quickly that their wings are impossible to see with the human eye and are just a blur. The maximum wingbeat recorded was **90 beats per second** for a hummingbird living in tropical South America. While hovering, hummingbirds' fluttering wings make the strange sound that gives them their name.

No Need to Land

After leaving its nest as a youngster, the **sooty tern** is thought to stay in the air continuously for **3-10 years** until it returns to its breeding colony as an adult. It doesn't even settle on the sea to feed, instead it catches fish or squid at the surface while hovering or seizes them in mid-air as they jump.

Biggest Wings

The **wandering albatross** of the southern oceans has the biggest wingspan of any living bird. Its mighty wings average a whopping **2.54-3.51m** (8ft 4in-11½ ft) at full stretch - that's wider than a car!

Swifts fly up to 1000km (620 miles) a day to find food for their nestlings.

Hummingbirds can fly backwards.

Migrating Artic terns fly halfway around the world.

Odd One Out

Look carefully at these bird images. Can you spot the odd one out in each group?

Peacock

A

B

C

Gentoo penguin

A   B   C

A   B   C

Flamingo

The black woodpecker pecks 12,000 times a day.

Bird Brainteaser

Can you fit the bird names below into the crossword? Each name will only fit in one place.

PARROT

SWAN

ROBIN

SEAGULL

OWL

PENGUIN

The grey parrot is the most talkative bird.

Answers on pages 76–77

Super Senses

The ostrich has the largest eyes of any living land animal.

Which bird can see the best? And who has the greatest hearing? Discover the answers to these questions and lots more below.

Looking Around

The **Eurasian woodcock** has the greatest field of vision of any bird. As well as being able to see 360 degrees, because of the high position of its eyes it can see above itself without having to move its head.

Birds have the best colour vision of any group of animals on Earth.

Acute Hearing

Although difficult to know for sure, it is likely that **barn owls** have the best hearing of all birds. These stealthy creatures can catch live prey in total darkness being guided by sounds alone.

Nocturnal birds such as **owls** have the best night time vision. Their eyes have lots of light-sensitive cells meaning they can see extremely well in the dark.

Sense of Smell

Most birds have a poor sense of smell but a small number of species rely on smell to find food so have large areas of their brain devoted to this sense. The **New Zealand kiwis** can sniff out worms and slugs amongst leaves and in soil.

Which Way?

The **oilbird** from South America and certain **cave swiftlets** living in Southeast Asia use echolocation, the echoes of their own sounds, to detect obstacles in their path. They nest in caves and even in total darkness, and at great speeds, they're able to sense the walls of the caves and so avoid flying into them.

A peregrine falcon can spot a pigeon over 8km (5 miles) away.

An oilbird in Ecuador

Bird Athletes

Hummingbirds are essentially incapable of walking.

Athletic birds are capable of running, flying and swimming. Read about some of their records below.

Speedy Swimming
The gold medal for fastest swimming goes to the **gentoo penguin**. It can reach speeds of up to **36 km/h** (22 mph) during short bursts of 'flying' underwater.

Diving Records
Emperor penguins can dive deeper than any other bird. Most of their dives are **100-200m** but the deepest on record is an amazing **565m** (1854ft).

The award for longest dive also goes to the **emperor penguin**. Two dives have been recorded at **22 minutes** each which is much longer than the average dive time for this species of **3-6 minutes**.

Running Records

The **ostrich** wins the award for fastest runner. In 1964 a male ostrich was timed at **72 km/h** (45 mph) over a distance of **732m** (2400ft) – this would be fast enough to win most horse races. At slower speeds of **50 km/h** (30 mph) most ostriches can run for about 30 minutes without apparently tiring.

Roadrunners can turn without slowing down. at right angles

The ostrich has the longest stride of any bird.

The **roadrunner** is the fastest runner of all flying birds. It can clock speeds of up to **42 km/h** (26 mph).

Walking Trick

Storm petrels are the only birds that are seemingly able to walk on water. They feed on small animals which they pluck from the sea while pattering on the surface. They are, in fact, wind-hovering which is flying slowly into the wind while trailing their feet in the sea.

Super Sudoku

Each bird can only appear once in each row, column and box.

Work out which bird is missing from each square to solve this Sudoku puzzle.

 Bald eagle
 Sparrow
 Duck
 Kingfisher

The American bald eagle can carry prey as large as a deer.

The South American hoatzin has an unfortunate claim to fame. Cross out all the words below that appear twice and the remaining words will reveal what it is.

BEAK

~~NEST~~ ~~EGG~~

SMELLIEST ~~FLY~~

BIRD ~~EGG~~ ~~CLAWS~~

IN ~~BEAK~~ ~~FEATHERS~~

THE ~~FLY~~ ~~FEATHERS~~

WORLD ~~NEST~~

~~CLAWS~~

Most small birds in the wild only live for 2-5 years.

The South American hoatzin is the

Smelliest bird in the world.

Answers on pages 76-77

65

Amazing Amphibians

Amphibians can be found almost anywhere there is a source of fresh water. Let's find out more about these remarkable creatures.

Record Breaker

The largest amphibian in the world is the **Chinese giant salamander** which lives in mountain streams in China. The average adult is **1.14m** (45in) long but one record-breaker was measured at **1.8m** (71in).

The Siberian salamander can survive temperatures as low as −56°C (−69°F).

The smallest amphibian is the *Paedophryne amanuensis* **frog** which measures just **0.77cm** (1/3 in). This tiny creature has a high-pitched call which sounds more like an insect than a frog.

On the Attack

Many newts and salamanders can secrete poison from glands in their skin but the **painted salamander** of Western USA is known to spray poisonous chemicals at its predators. It squirts the toxin from the base of its tail and can hit a target in the face from **2.1m** (7ft) away. Not bad considering it's only **15-18cm** (6-7in) long!

A poisonous fire salamander

Cute Creature

This strange looking amphibian is an **axolotl**, which comes from an Aztec word meaning 'water monster'. Axolotls are found in Mexico and live permanently in the water.

200 million years ago giant amphibians up to 4m (13ft) long lived on Earth.

Red-eyed tree frog

Alpine newt

A cane toad lays 30,000–35,000 eggs per spawning.

Ever Changing

Many species of salamander are able to regrow missing eyes, limbs or tails. The process takes a few months and the new pieces may grow back a different colour and shape.

Frog Jumble

How many of each colour poison-arrow frog can you count in the jumble below? Write your answers in the boxes.

RED

BLUE

GREEN

Poison-arrow frogs are brightly coloured to warn predators they are dangerous.

Which of the words below can't be made out of the letters in AMPHIBIAN? Draw a circle around them.

Which Words?

NAME

BRAIN

BIN

HIP

NAP

MINI

BEAM

PHONE

HAND

> 75–100 new species of frogs and toads are formally described every year.

PAIN

Answers on pages 76–77

Frogs and Toads

Frogs and toads can be found all over the world. Let's find out more about these jumping amphibians.

World's Biggest
The **African giant** or **Goliath frog** is the largest of all frogs and toads. Found in West Africa, this creature certainly lives up to its names measuring in at **30cm** (12in) long.

Fire-bellied toads have eyes with heart-shaped pupils.

Giant Leaps
There is a big variation between frogs and toads and individuals when it comes to jumping ability. And it isn't necessarily the largest creatures that make the longest jumps. Indeed, the current world record-holder is the **South African sharp-nosed frog** which is only **5.5-6.6cm** (2^{1}/$_{8}$-2^{1}/$_{2}$ in) long.

The golden poison-arrow frog carries enough poison to kill 20,000 mice.

See-through Skin

Some frogs have transparent skin which means their internal organs can be seen by the naked eye. These so-called **glass frogs** are found in the cloud and rainforests of Central and South America.

Take a Breath

All frogs and toads have fully working lungs but they are also able to absorb oxygen through their skin, from either water or air. The best at breathing through its skin is the **Lake Titicaca frog** which can stay underwater for long periods of time.

Deadly Toxins

Frogs and toads don't bite or sting but some secrete poison from their skin. The **golden poison-arrow frogs** of western Columbia are the most poisonous. Their skin is so highly toxic that scientists have to wear thick gloves when picking them up.

There are more than 6600 species of frogs and toads.

Speedy Spotting

How quickly can you spot the 10 differences between these two pictures?

Tick a box as you find each difference.

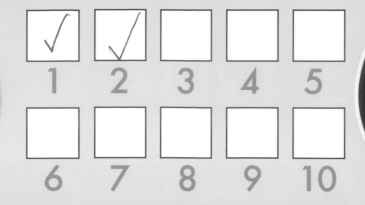

How quick were you?
0-2 minutes: Awesome!
3-5 minutes: Pretty good!
More than 5 minutes: Not bad!

Answers on pages 76-77

Animal Quiz

How much have you learnt from reading this annual? Find out by answering the questions below!

Tick true or false to answer each question.

1 The largest living land animal is the African elephant.

✓ True ☐ False

2 Reptiles lay their eggs on land.

☐ ☐
True False

3 Octopuses are able to open car doors.

☐ ☐
True False

4 The smallest bat is about the size of a bumble bee.

☐ True ☐ False

5 The tiger-shark has been nicknamed 'garbage-can shark'.

✓ ☐
True False

74

6

The flamingo is the largest living bird in the world.

☐ True ☒ **False**

7

Most dinosaurs were carnivores.

☐ True ☐ False

8

A crocodilian's jaw can be kept closed with a rubber band.

☑ True ☐ False

9

Whales are fish.

☐ True ☐ false

10

The tarantula is the world's largest spider.

☐ True ☐ false

How did you do?

1-3 Correct: Try again!

4-7 Correct: Good effort!

8-10 Correct: Animal expert!

Answers on pages 76-77

ANSWERS

Page 10: Animal Hunt

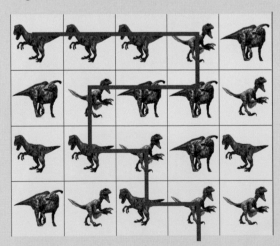

Page 11: Super Sequences

1. Tiger
2. Elephant
3. Dolphin
4. Horse

Page 16: Mammal Match

Giraffe 4.

Page 17: Colour Code

Fastest over a long distance.

Page 22: Picture Puzzle

Page 23: Dinosaur Words

Some words you can make are: RUN, DIN, OAR, SUN, RAN, SAND, SON, RADIOS, SOUNDS.

Pages 26-27: Underwater Observation

Page 30: Make a Match

A and F, B and K, C and H, E and J, G and I. Fish D isn't part of a pair.

Page 31: Underwater Words

1. FISH
2. CORAL
3. SEA
4. WATER
5. SEAWEED
6. ROCK
7. REEF
8. SAND

Page 36: Tortoise Time

B, F, A, E, C, D.

Page 37: Bits and Pieces

1 – F, 2 – E, 3 – D, 4 – A, 5 – C.

Page 42: Who is it?

1 – D, 2 – E, 3 – A, 4 – B, 5 – C.

Page 43: Hidden Fact

It is the largest lizard in the world.

Page 48: Which Way?

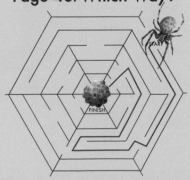

Page 49: On the Move

A = 10, B = 14, C = 12. The ants should take path B.

Page 52: Who's Hiding?

A – bee, B – butterfly, C – beetle, D – spider.

Page 53: Spot the Sequence

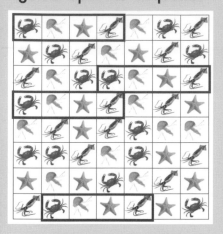

Page 58: Odd One Out

1 – C, 2 – A, 3 – B.

Page 59: Bird Brainteaser

PARROT / PENGUIN / ROBIN / OWL / SWAN / SEAGULL

Page 64: Super Sudoku

Page 65: Word Play

The South American hoatzin is the smelliest bird in the world.

Page 68: Frog Jumble

Red – 6, blue – 5, green – 7.

Page 69: Which Words?

NAME, BEAM, HAND, PHONE and BRAIN can't be made from the letters in AMPHIBIAN

Pages 72-73: Speedy Spotting

Pages 74-75: Animal Quiz

1. True.
2. True.
3. False - they can open screw top jars.
4. True.
5. True.
6. False - it's the ostrich.
7. False – most dinosaurs were herbivores.
8. True.
9. False - whales are mammals.
10. False - it's a species of huntsman spider.